Letters from a
LOST UNCLE

MERVYN PEAKE

(from polar regions)

Methuen · London

FIRST LETTER-

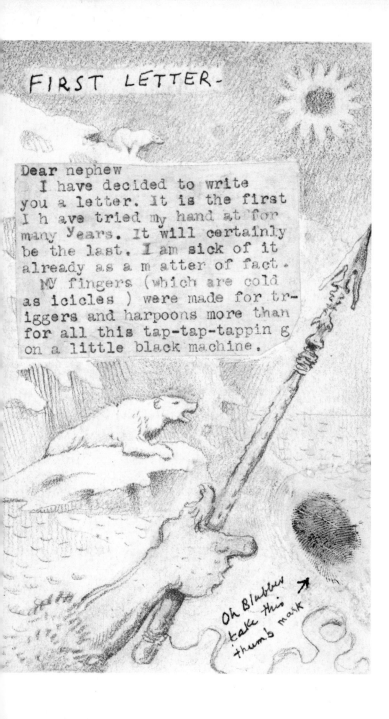

Dear nephew
    I have decided to write
you a letter. It is the first
I h ave tried my hand at for
many Years. It will certainly
be the last. I am sick of it
already as a m atter of fact .
    MY fingers (which are cold
as icicles) were made for tr-
iggers and harpoons more than
for all this tap-tap-tappin g
on a little black machine.

Oh Blubber take this thumb mark

Pickle my blubber ! but it makes mee feel like a womank,
writing this letter to England
when there is so m uch danger
and excitement in the arctic air
to be getting on with;

Not only this, but what with
Jackson to be unloaded before
he curls up to sleep, and what
with my leg-spike to polish...

I had better start by describing
myself as best I can.   It will be easier for you to picture me and underst-
and my point of view.   In fact I will
do a drawing of myself after I have gi-
ven you a few measurements.   I would
be about six foot and six inches ·
high in my sock if I hadnt worn it
out.   My distance round the middle
doesn't matter so much but it makes
quite a journey there and back.   It
won't be easy to draw myself as I ca-
n't remember my face very well.   I'll
do it on the next page as there'll
be more room.   To fill up the
space above, I'll draw the sea-elephant I skinned a week or so ago.   It
had rather a beastly taste, when I
had fried it, but Jackson appeared
to enjoy it.   *(I'd forgotten that I'd
already drawn a sea-elephant — not that it
matters.) Oh no! it was an elephant seal*

I think I look like this but as I broke my only looking-glass twelve years ago you must remember it is from memory only.

This is what artists call a full-length self-portrait. In the distance is the crag which I climbed before I lost my leg. No one else knows the way up.

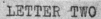

the iglob will beg tunnel didle I favour

LETTER TWO

I wont have much time for write-
ing this time as I find I'm on a
piece of floating ice the size
of Kent. It has started moving
in the opposite direction to where I want to go, so I have sent
Jackson out to get the kyak ready
and then we'll paddle a-way to
the North-East.

It looks as though the next
few days will be the most dangerous of my life. That is really
why i Have decided to write you
this letter which will be a kind
of diary 1 suppose. If I get killed
or anything, perhaps these pages
may be found, although what the good
they'll be to anyone, I cant imagine, unless I find the WHITE LION
first. Not that I intend to get
killed. Hags blubber ! I'm not sea-
soned for nothing.

Here is a drawing of Jackson so
that you can understand him. He
has been my retainer for many
years and has no conversation;
but I would'nt swap him for six
tins of condensed milk or a jug
of hot rum.

By the way I am writing to you
from an igloo in the polar waste.
Now I must end this letter (why
did I ever begin it?)and see if
the kyak is ready, because I am.
By the way, I have'nt made a single mistake with my tap-tap-ta-
pping on this page, have I?
   ·O blubbe r it !.

We've got a light on inside the igloo, so from the outside you'd see our shadows through the ——

Im still in the igloo although
it's next day. A blizzard sprang up almost as I finish ed my
last letter, and it has been
howling outside like a hungry
animal ever since. Pickle me !
but I can hardly feel the typewriter, my hands are so cold.
  Jackson is lying beside me
snoring heavily with one of his
eyelids twitching every now and
again. But it is getting warmer
because i have crammed up the
entrance ofmy igloo with the hides of beasts. And I have a good
fire burning as well. The place
is a bit smoky, but 1 can still
see Jackson.
  It will be quite impossible
for me to embark today, even though the island of ice that I'm
on is being driven across the
water as fast as a ship.

Irritating as it is to be blown
off one's course, yet it does give
me the chance of going on with
this letter.
     Perhaps you have never heard
of me before ? I would'(nt be sur-
prised. Explorers are soon forgotten ; even by their relations.
In fact especially by their relations,I should say. Not that I
ever write any letters home. This
is the first- so if it reaches
you, take care of it. Not only
c ould I never start this sort of
literary business all over again,
but also I hope there will be vi-
tal information near the end of it,
about the WhiTE LIUN, · · ·

(Jackson has
fallen asleep and
looks even sillier
than ever.)

which you can take to the Natural
History Museum in South Kensington-
if its still there.

sea- → leopard

← elephant-
seal.

and the sea-leopard stew to prepare for supper, i cant think
why I began this letter tonight
of all times.

You wont know what this is yet, but I'll explain latter.

Nevertheles I am your Uncle, I
suppose, and must fall to the task.

For I have a reason. I will explain about it later, but for the moment I will tell you one thing only so as to keep you on tender-hooks.It is this. At the back of my reason for writing to you -at the back of it all- at the back of my m ind- at the back of everything I believe in, is the WHITE LION; The LION on the stamp- the Emperor of the Snows.

This is a copy of part of the stamp. only bigger + freer

Even if the drawing of me isnt
a speaking likeness, I do know that I have only one eye, (that works)
one leg, and a single mind.   I get
along very well; very well indeed an-
d I can't bear sympathy.

As I can explain things better by
making drawings as I go along - which I delight in doing - I do not want
you to think that they are simply to
please you.   If you like them, that-
s all the better but I would do them
anyway.   This is a good fat book with any number of blank leaves, so
there is no fear of my not having e-
nough paper, however many drawings I
put on a page.

For instance, from where I sit I can see my right foot perfectly, and my leg-spike, too, with the inside of the igloo, beyond - so as an example, I will make a drawing of it, before I continue.

It is getting rather stuffy, and I think I will loosen the hides in the igloo-tunnel to let a little of the blizzard in.

As you may have noticed I have a leg-spike and what with this and my experience of violent things I can deal with most emergencies.   For instance, last Monday when an Arctic ~~polar~~ wolf sprang at me, skinny with hunger and his teeth shining, I had only to do this:-

and all was over.

My leg-spike originally belo-
nged to a sword-fish that attacked
me in my kyak. We had a desperat-
e encounter during which I lost my
leg and he lost the spike off his
nose, as well as his life. It occ-
urred to me at once that it was jus-
t the same length as my missing leg
and I fitted it on that same evening. (with pain and difficulty)

Of course I can't walk as fast as
before but it serves me in many way-
s, particularly in preventing me
from slipping on the ice.

Sorry about
these blotches but I've
just cut my finger —
but it's almost mended
with a small
skin bandage wound
it.

My fire has almost gone out - I
have been so busy writing and drawing.   How cold it has become.   The
gale is still howling outside,and I
have let too much of it in through
the funnel.   I will end this letter
now as I want to get warm.   About
this time next month, I'll have
built another igloo miles and miles to the east from here - if this
tempest hasn't carried me too far
astray.   Then I will be able to
continue this letter, when the icy, dripping, bear-infested forests
of petrified pine have been explored, and the jagged mountains climbed.   Then perhaps I can explain
to you want it is exactly that I
am searching for - how I left home and why I am telling you all this.
Goodnight.

Floods and storms have happened
to me since my last letter.   It
doesn't seem quite so bad writing
to you this time - not that I really enjoy it very much.   But as I'
ve explained I have a reason for
what I do, and must persevere.

I am no longer in the igloo of
course, but am manny, many leagues
further to the west and the floating ice that was the size of Kent is
left far behind.   The last I saw
of it was from my kyak, with the
sun rising and staining it all pink
and cold as it spread away from me
and right over the horizon.   When
the tempest was at its height the
wind changed direction and blew the
ice back to almost exactly where we
started from.

But that was several weeks ago a-
nd the storms that I have encounte-
red since then were huger still.
For I came to the outskirts of a
forest of trees that had been froz-
en into skeletons that never put
forth leaves. And as I entered the

forest the snow poured down, until only our heads were above it.
And a great wind galloped out of
the mountains of clanging ice that

stood around the forest, until the
cold trees roared as though ever-
y one of them had a throat.   Then
came the sleet and Hailstorms that
snapped their branches off, one by
one to toss about in the wild snow.

But I'll tell you all about that journey later (if I've got tim-
e).   For the moment I will content
myself with a few drawings of the
beasts I met with on the way, and
also a drawing of the cabin I have
built, and in which I am now writing you this letter.

This is a Moose
(the Knotted-tail kind)

Sorry about my
thumb-mark
again →

This is the cabin which I
promised to draw. It also sh-
ows you the kind of landscape
that surrounds it.

4'TH LETTER

I am very comfortable this evening with my explorations for th-
e day completed.   I have a feeling inside me that I am getting
nearer and nearer to the white Lion.   As I feel so contented I think I will expand a bit in my letter.
It is the first time I have looked
forward to continuing it.   I suppose its because I like seeing how
many words I have already written
and all the drawings I've made.

What I have been meaning to tell
you all about is how I started this
wandering life.   Then you can see
me in what old men call perspective, which only means that you can
understand why I do certain things
because you know the things I did
before.   Anyway, I'll be as quick
as I can with theis part because
the reason for this talk is the Lion on the Stamp and everything
else is only padding as a matter
of fact.

Anyway you will soon come out
of the Distant Past and into the
Present again.   As far as I'm conc-
erned its the Future that matters
most.   I am longing to tell you a-
bout my Project, but the time is
not quite ripe.

Oh, Blubber! I've been such a long time without a drawing. It comes as a great relief to stop prodding at this little black machine, and start making pictures again.   There is a Polar beetle crawling through the door of my hut - so I might as well draw that.

I feel very much better now that I have finished the beetle. Where was I in my letter?   Oh yes, I was going to tell you about my past.

I was born in Tulse Hill but ran away within a week. They found me in Finsbury and brought me back and strapped me down in a cradle,

When I was old enough to go
to school. I drank so much ink   .
on the first day that I was ser-
iously ill until I was old enough to leave.

Then I ran away from home
but got tired of being hungry
so I returned one night and
éát ate my way through the
larder.   I was ill again, this time until I was twenty-two,
when I married.

I had soon grown a beard which I have never since shaved off.
My wife despised it.

At about this time I began
to collect different kinds of
insects, mushrooms and rats.
The best place for them from
the point of view of their hea-
lth was the lounge.   I began
to notice that my wife was not
so considerate as she used to
be, so I had my meals out, an-
d usually slept in Cannon Street Station.   Between times I
went a lot to the Natural History Museum in South Kensington
or made drawings of the four lions in Trafalgar Square.   I
now realize that all the lions
were exactly the same so I might have saved myself a lot of
time.   What with the Lions, and
the Natural History Museum, I wh-
ipped my imagination into a fren-
zy.   A hungry longing to see
the world overtook me and I decided to leave my native land, and,
I decided, come what may, that
I would set sail for the tropics

When my wife (who looked
like this, poor thing, and
still does, I expect)

heard of my intentions, the end of
her nose grew as cold as ice,
and her ears burned like beet-
roots.   She was very, very angry and when all her brothers · · ·↙

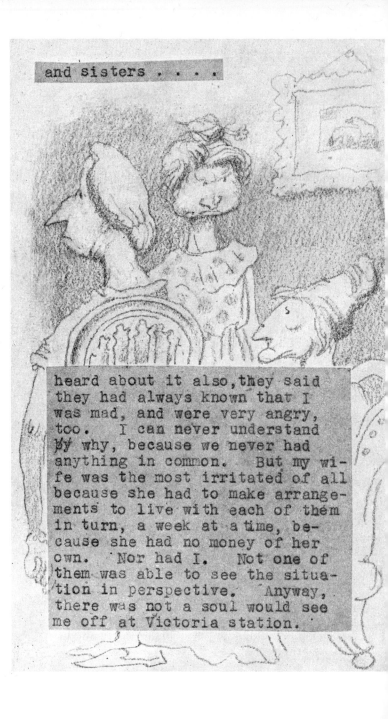

heard about it also, they said
they had always known that I
was mad, and were very angry,
too.   I can never understand
why why, because we never had
anything in common.   But my wife was the most irritated of all
because she had to make arrange-
ments to live with each of them
in turn, a week at a time, because she had no money of her
own. 'Nor had I.   Not one of
them was able to see the situa-
tion in perspective. 'Anyway,
there was not a soul would see
me off at Victoria station.

I was soon at the coast and on
board the s.s.Em, a sprightly
craft, with orange-and-blue funn-
els. Whether her name was short
øfor Empire or Emu I never found
out. It always seemed to me to
be rather brief for a ship of her
length. Nevertheless, the food
was very good, and a welcome change after my wife's cookery,for I
had spent my last three days under my own roof. No more roofs
for me ⌐ not the plaster sort, any
way.

Not many weeks after I had gone
on board the weather had changed
into something so golden that I
took my stiff collar off and threw
it into the sea. Since then I
have never worn a collar and I

shall never start that sort of
nonsense again.

Many and various things
happened to me at the coloured
ports; in the black harbours, and
up creeks of fever; or where the
great trees along the banks of
tropical rivers bent over our
ship as we steamed along down
endless tunnels of deep green;
the fruit and nuts fell plonk,
plonk, rat-tat-tat as they ~~first~~
struck the deck, for they were
always being knocked off the ov-
erhanging branches by the masts
of the s.s.Em.   I remember how
the monkeys, and the great apes
would swing like shadows across
the green gloom above us,catchi-
ng hold of the mastheads with
their long hairy arms and ~~and~~
swinging back again into the
riverside trees.   And all the
frightful noise of their chattering and the screaming of par-
rots that made the air bloodsh-
ot with their wings :

and then there were the days
when I leaned on the ship's railing, and gazed over the ocean,
rubbing my beard and smoking the
pipe I carved out of the leg of
my wife's favourite arm chair.
I used to meditate quite a lot
which will surprise you I expect
for as you know I am a man of
action.

One summer evening I was pondering thus, over the ship's railing.   Below me in the ocean
a shark swam swiftly along-
side the ship and I was amus-
ing myself by throwing it little pieces of cheese which it
cought cleverly in its mouth:

Beyond the shark, the reflection
of an enormous moon bobbed about
on the waves.   Suddenly I
stopped throwing cheese for an
idea struck me - for I suddenly
realized that I had never asked
anyone where the ship was sailing
to.

There was no one else on deck
so I couldn't make enquiries.
I had been pondering so long
that it must have been nearly
midnight.   You see, when I left
England I had been so excited
to get away that I had **never**
troubled to ask which way the
ship was steering - except that
it was towards the tropics.

I went down to my cabin, the
cheese being finished, but
couldn't get to sleep, it was
so hot.   The negro (whom I
shared the cabin with) was
snoring loudly, so I shook
him, but he only turned over
and began again worse than
before.

So I got up and went up on
deck again, this time in my
dressing-gown.   Imagine my
excitement when I reached the
railing, when I saw, away across the moonlit sea, a line of
glittering mountains.   At once,
and almost without thinking, I
made one of the most important
decisions of my life.

I ran to my cabin, got dres-
sed, put on my hat and threw my
eiderdown over my arm.   I was
half way back to the deck again
when I remembered my looking-
glass which I went back for.
When I reached the deck I left
the eiderdown hanging over the
rail and with my looking-glass
in my jacket pocket I rushed
into the dining saloon and pulled a long table out through
the door and into the moonlight.   The only other things
I needed were an oar, which I
found in a lifeboat, and a ch-
-air.   I had to return to the
saloon for this, and then I was
complete.   Tying the chair and
table together with a bit of
rope I threw them overboard and
jumped after them with the oar
in one hand and the eiderdown
wound around my stomach.

also my typewriter and camera
and several other things.

I landed with a great splash
and swallowed a lot of sea water, but was soon scrambling onto the table which was floating
quite near with the chair tied
on. They were both bobbing in
the waves. I pulled the chair
after me. The four legs of
the table were sticking up in
the air in a helpless sort of
way, for it had landed on its
back. I heaved the chair into
the middle and sat down on it,
with the oar across my knees
and the wet eiderdown spread
out around my feet to dry in
the moonlight. When I looked
around, the old s.s. Em was far
away, and I was left all alone
on my table-boat on a wide ocean.

    I think this would make a
good drawing, so I'll do it on
the next page where there's
more room. (on a bigger scale)

I suppose I must have looked
something like this.　As you
can see I had not yet lost my
other leg in those early days.
Pickle-my-carcase! how innocent
I was!

That last drawing has tak-
en me so long that I must go
out and stretch my legs, or rather my leg, for my spike never
needs stretching.   That's another advantage that it has which I hadn't thought of before.

(OH! Beuberation!)

I am continuing the letter.
It is a lovely night outside
the cabin, the Arctic sun bur-
-ning like a hundred different
coloured torches with a Polar
bear on top of an iceberg, im-
mediately in front of it and
looking as though it's been cut
out of black cardboard.   It's
what they call 'silhouetted',
I think - (not that the bear
would know.)   After stretching
my leg I came in and grilled
myself a walrus cutlet.   Very
delicious.   I shall continue
now with more enthusiasm from
where I left off.   Isn't it
wonderful - I'm beginning to
enjoy writing to you?   I did-
n't like you much at first.
But you wait till I get some
news of the White Lion.   Then
I'll really WRITE.

By the way, the gravy-stain on
the last page was Jacksons
fault. Wh att a clumsy beast
he is.

Well, there i was, all those
years ago.   (I am sorry about
the new gravy stain - that is
Jackson again!) - as I say,
there I was, all those years
ago, having jumped off the
boat and sitting on the moonlit table, tossing on the waves,
a bit lonely with the deep sea
muttering around me.

Yet after a bit I began to
realize that this was just the
sort of thing for which I had
been craving in London.   Why
had I left England?   For this
sort of thing, of course.   Then,
instead of feeling lonely I felt
happier than I had ever felt in
my life before.

·I sang aloud (a thing I sel-
dom do) and swarms of fishes
lifted their moonlit heads out
of the water to listen to me,
their eyes like shillings, and
it was only

after I'd no more breath left
that they lowered themselves
into the depth of the sea.

I began to row the table towards the mountains on the skyline. It was a slow business, as you can imagine, with such a craft beneath me, and it was dawn before I reached the land and stepped off the table onto a beach of red sand with turtle dogs littered all over it (asleep), one of whom is now sleeping beside me - Jackson, in fact. I could see that he would be useful at once as a beast of burden - and possibly as a friend.

As you can see there was not much life in J when I first found him.
Even so he didn't want to come with me at first. I was irritated

night from the start.

Eiderdown

Orchid stalks

Then I strode into the hint-
erland after having made a tear
in the eiderdown and pulled
out all the feathers. I did this
because I had discovered a damp
valley full of orchids, and I
filled my eiderdown full of them.
    It is their stalks that I smoke
and very delicious they are too,
I would have you know.

This page is
absolutely wasted
thanks to Jackson who
has just put his stupid,
grubby foot all over it
just as I was going
to start.
Blubber him!

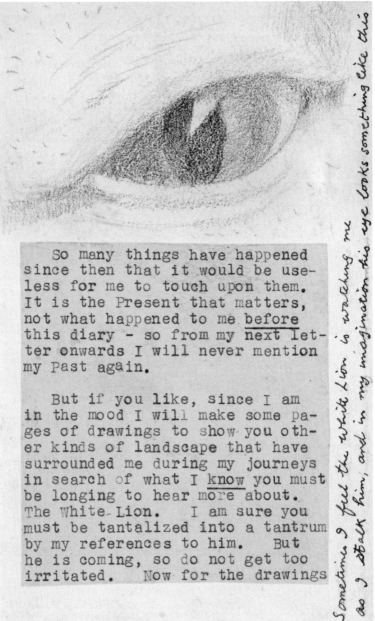

So many things have happened
since then that it would be use-
less for me to touch upon them.
It is the Present that matters,
not what happened to me before
this diary - so from my next letter onwards I will never mention
my Past again.

But if you like, since I am
in the mood I will make some pages of drawings to show you other kinds of landscape that have
surrounded me during my journeys
in search of what I know you must
be longing to hear more about.
The White Lion.   I am sure you
must be tantalized into a tantrum
by my references to him.   But
he is coming, so do not get too
irritated.   Now for the drawings

Sometimes I feel the white lion is watching me
as I stalk him, and in my imagination his eye looks something like this

This is the kind
of thing I saw
quite a lot of in
my early days —

It was heavy going in these regions

but quite exciting. I stayed for 3 years.

I named this waterfall after Jackson
who had worked very hard that day — but
afterwards I wished I hadn't —

These are the kind of creatures I saw a lot of. In the left-hand bottom corner is a baby crocodile coming out of its egg.

FIFTH LETTER

What a long letter my last one was, but now we must get to the point. I promised in my last letter not to refer to my Past again, so I can't tell you about the extraordinary escape I had from a snow-serpent five days ago (it was about as long as the distance between two lamp-posts). It is most aggravating not to be able to recount the experience of how I pinned it to a pine-tree with my leg-spike, and how I could not remove my leg or myself for over three days because it died so slowly. For my leg-spike is fixed on to me so efficiently that I could not detach myself, and-- oh, blubber! how wicked his eyes looked with me only just out of reach of his flickering fangs! How glad I was when at last he closed his little red eyes, and his poisoned tongue stopped trembling for ever and I removed my leg-spike from his throat!

How hungry I was, too!

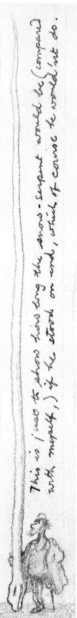

This is (was to show how long the snow-serpent would be (compared with myself,) if he stood on end, which it would not do.

This blotch is
washing-up water —
sorry.

I am now many miles further
to the North-East and am writing from a cave in a gaunt hill
side. Yesterday was weary beyond belief. There was nothing in the landscape except
snow. When Jackson and I sat
down to rest we could see our
foot-prints stretching back to
the edge of the world.

Picture of me getting the
feel of the dawn outside my cave.

There was no point in building an igloo last night for the weather is not quite so cold. At the bottom of this hill is a kind of frozen bay and Jackson collected a sackfull of broken planks, the remains of some shipwreck, I suppose. They made an excellent fire.   He has always been quite willing to help although I have never seen him smile.   Also he does not mind me hammering nails into his back to hang things on, It doesn't hurt him any more than when you have your fingernails cut, but some beasts might well take exception, nevertheless.

It is Jackson who carries my camera (a heavy thing and perhaps my most precious possession).   For it is my Ambition above all others to photograph the White Lion: it will prove that I have seen him.   Perhaps I will be doomed to disappointment and will <u>NEVER</u> see him. Oh, blubber! that would capsize everything.

'And who on earth is this
White Lion?' you will be ask-
ing.   I will tell you, nephew.   He is the Lord of Snow.
There have been strange rumours about him.   Rumours that
have spread across the world.
Hags blubber! I've met with
them everywhere from snow to
burning sand.

I'm approaching his domin-
ion.   I am sure of it.   I
have never felt as I feel now
- so certain of being near him
- for I've developed any number of instincts which I never
had in England.   And they all
point to one thing - that I'm
on his tail - or very nearly.
I keep an eye very wide open,
and even my leg-spike seems to
stalk along, as though it had
a brain inside it.

You will understand, unless you are very stupid, how exciting it is after so many years spent in searching for the White Lion, to feel so close to him. I began my search so very long ago. I have moved this way and - that: gradually, gradually, this way and that, but mostly this way. I scoured the tropics - he wasn't there. Cancer and Capricorn had never heard of him. I scrutinized every inch of the equator and he wasn't there, either.

I pursued ~~after~~ him in a
hundred ways.   I have built
canoes out of birchwood.

I carved dug-outs from ced-
arwood

I have made coracles out of
animals' skin

and have searched the~~se~~ dangerous rivers

I have made wigwams

and cabins of pine

and have lived in hollow trees
and mountainous caves

I have searched the forests
that surround all these

And steered my raft among the
coughing waves.

Sometimes I thought I was
nearing his boundaries only
to be disappointed.   I found
his stamp seven times during
my wanderings.   Once it was
on a letter which a pigmy
dropped on the ground when a
crocodile chased him up a tree.
This stamp, with his image on
it only helped to inflame my
imagination.   I searched all
the harder .   Oh, Pickle my
blubber! but my wanderings
would fill a book as big as
the Bible.

    I must go to sleep now.
I'm sure something exciting is
going to happen tomorrow.

Next letter (6 th.)

It is nine o'clock at night.
I am very tired - and not very
much wanting to write. I had
thought that today was going
to be important - but nothing
has happened at all except
trudge, trudge, trudge, through
the blinding snow. Jackson
has been most irritating, stum-
bling over every little hump
of ground and having to be picked up. I stopped him to do
a drawing for a great black
sea was on our left some of
the way with peculiar icebergs
on it, but he kept moving just
when I got my pencil on the paper. Sometimes I wish I was
on my own.

<u>Next day</u> (seventh letter)

Nothing to report. I was
~~sure~~ something would happen to-
~~day.~~ Snow, snow, snow. Oh,
Blubber! I really am getting
sick of white as a colour.
Tired out. Don't think I'll
wash tonight.

Next evening. (Eighth)

Nothing to report. Jack-
son has a beastly cough. Am
very irritated.

Next evening. (9th)

I'm fed up. Jackson's
cough worse. Good<u>night</u>.

Next evening (Tenth).

I can't think why nothing
important is happening because
I am sure I am close to the
White ~~Lion~~. I can feel it in
every bone I've got - including
my leg-spike. There were seven
clues today, six of which I followed in turn. No good! I'll
pursue the last one tomorrow.
I'm sorry these last two letters have been so short.
Jackson's cough is better.
There's a funny green light
in the sky this evening. I
wonder what it means.

Four days later.

A very exciting day in-
deed has just happened to me.
Yesterday as I travelled over
the snow on a sledge I have
just made - (and which John-
son pulls) we suddenly heard
the sound of wailing.   We
were in an even more desolate
tract than usual, the snow
rising into great soft deathly
silent mountains.   But the
wailing grew louder and louder
in spite of the silence until
at last, just as it seemed all
about us, swarms of little
creatures appeared in the distance pouring themselves over
the hills and wringing their
hands as they ran.

I knew at once, of course,
that they were fleeing from
the scene of some Arctic tragedy.   The snow all around us
that had been so speckless was

black with them.   And then,
suddenly, they were all gone
and nothing remained except their little footmarks in the
snow, like smallpox.   A tremor
ran down my spine, for suddenly the silence had come again
and it was as white and empty
as the snowy hills before the
footmarks came.

    The waiting of the creatures
had disturbed the sea-elephants,
~~which~~ some of whom broke through
the icy ground, and pushed their
ugly heads through the snow where
it wasn't so thick in the val-
leys.   Then they began to bel-
low as though they were in pain,
or as though they also knew
that there was a tragedy happening somewhere which they had only just heard about.

Next week

I said in last weeks letter
that I had had an exciting day -
but when I look back on it now
it seems very dull.   This is
because since then I have been
in the thick of glory.   I will
tell you about it.   I haven't
been able to write to you during
the last few days because I've
had too much to do.   I meant to
write last night, but when I had
built my fire, I felt too tired.
And yet I couldn't sleep
either because all night long
I kept remembering my adven-
tures.   But I feel full of
energy this morning and have
just finished my breakfast of
penguins' eggs covered up with sea-leopard soup.   Also
I have bandaged up
all the wounds which
Jackson suffered
yesterday, as well as four of
my own.

TWELTH
LETTER.

In the dawn of yesterday I knew that there was something combustible in the air and my stomach felt like soda water.

First of all, as the sun began to heave itself, all lilac and green above the horizon of dark snow, I began to prepare my weapons - my camera, and to whet my sword-fish leg. Next I got Jackson ready. Even he seemed to know there was danger about, and he became even more clumsy than usual.

There was nothing really to show that the day would be dif-ferent from other ones. The deep snow covered the world as usual. Nevertheless the image of the White Lion, the fabulous and Only Lion to thrive in Arctic zones, possessed me and filled my mind until it seemed my brain was white with him.

We started out and as we
strode onwards the sun grew
bigger and bigger and redder
and redder.   At about nine
o'clock the snow got harder
under our feet and I took the
cork off my spike while we
rested.   At the same time I
filled my pipe with orchid
stalks, and it was delicious
to smoke such exclusive stuff
in the world wastes.   When
we started again we noticed
how quickly the snow hardened
step by step until there was
a greenish-blackish colour under our feet which was as hard
as marble, and my spike began
to make sparks as it clanged
on the ground.

Jackson began to be unsure
of his feet and slithered
here and there, and then, after
I had picked him up for the
twentyeth time, off he went
again, slithering across the
ice.   Suddenly I realized that
he was going faster and faster,
for it was downhill and nothing
could stop him.   But what was
worse, I saw that he was
heading for a great chasm.

How fast I ran after him I cannot say, but the sparks flew from the ice as though it was Guy Fawkes' Day, and I sounded like crockery being broken for a long time. The yawning chasm ahead looked as though it was rushing towards Jackson. Within a few moments he would plunge over the edge of the ice, and carry my precious belongings, and my camera, as well as himself over the glassy brink and down into the depths. I redoubled my sparks, and just as he was about to fly out into the ghastly darkness to be lost for ever, I gave a great leap and pinned him by his trousers to the ice. My leg-spike had just missed his scaly little leg, but his trousers were made out of strong whaleskin and did not tear at all. So there we were - breathless but safe on the brink of the chasm.

But how were we to get across?   It gaped below us, black
and deadly and as wide as a
tennis court.   It was no use
looking at Jackson.   He could-
n't help.   The silly way in
which he sat down and waited
with his eyes on me made me
angry.   But there was a new
trouble.   Out of the sky
came a swarm of Arctic vultures - huge birds with bod-
ies as big as dogs'.   They
swooped with hideous speed
upon us, and only turned aside
with gaping claws and beaks
wide open like scissors when
they were all but in our hair.

Up they shot again in a
cloud of wicked feathers until
they were only specks in the
freezing sky.

Just when we thought we were
free of them down they came a-
gain with screams of hunger.
This time I lay on my back with
my leg-spike in the air to pro-
tect myself.

But they saw it in time and
swerved over my head, in fact
one of their long grizzly
plumes fell across my face.

This time as the great
birds shot past us, I noticed
that as they sped across the
chasm before they lifted in
flight and soared once more
into the zenith. Then I remembered something. These
dreadful fowl will only feed
on carrion. They were wait-
ing for us to die. I had an
idea and told J. to tie half
of our belongings to one of
his legs and I tied the rest
of the things to one of my
legs - to my only leg, in
fact - and we lay down flat
on the ice at the edge of the
chasm and pretended to be dead,
after I had explained over 5
times to J. what he was to do.

Hags blubber! how slow he
was.

Down came the vultures from
the sky again while we lay
stiff and still.   We watched
them out of the corners of
our half-closed eyes until
they were just above us.   Their wings rattled aloud,their
mouths were wide and their
long scraggy necks trembled
with greed.

At that moment we sprang to our feet and before the vultures could stop their rushing flight, we jumped at the nearest birds and, catching hold of their ankles, were carried across the chasm.

We were heavy for them, of
course, so that they were
only just able to get across,
their wings beating frantic-
ally.   This suited us very
well, for it meant that when
we let go of their legs on
the other side of the chasm
we had only a few feet to fall,

As soon as we let go the
vultures shot up to the sky
so rapidly that they were
out of sight before we had
got to our feet. We never
saw them again, nor any of
their hideous tribe. We had
too much life in us to suit
their tastes.

By now it was nearly ten
o'clock. The sun, like a
crimson balloon seemed to
be hanging just above our
heads with the sky a long
way behind it. But it gave
out no heat; or if it did, I
never felt it and J. was
shaking badly.

as we trudged onwards (I
forgot to say that our sledge
had been smashed by a moose)

the ground became knobbly, and
the ice gave place to softer
and softer ground until we
were once again in deep snow.
It was dangerous country; I
could feel it in every bone of
my body, especially my spine
and shoulder-blades.   I looked about me piercingly.   J.
hadn't felt anything at all
and trudged on at my side with
his irritatingly little feet
making marks in the snow the
      shape of fishes.

By now the snow was so
deep that I fixed the cork
into my swordfish leg which
made walking easier.

It had been a still and
silent day, but all of a
sudden there was a kind of
rustly sound, a shuffling
commotion in the snow all
about us, and then the first
icy, slithering, terrible
breath of a perilous wind.

I stood still at once.   It
was not an ordinary wind -
because it didn't seem to
come from any particular
direction, but was more
like gooseflesh all over
the earth.   I called Jackson
to me with a sharp word of
command.   The gooseflesh got
worse and the snow began to shift
under our feet so that it was
difficult to keep our balance.
There was only one thing to do
in that great waste, and that
was to dig.   Within a few minutes we had scooped a deep hole,
and although the snow had to be
baled out continuously, we were
more protected below the surface.   I stood up and peered
over the top and I all but lost
my bowler hat for a curly draught of air nearly plucked it
from my head.   As I say, it was
a curling draught, for I noticed
in the short time I had with my
head above the edge, that there
were great blankets of snow in
the air that floated and waved
and growing faster and faster
in their flight began to circle
round and round a white pillar
that was growing up in their
middle.

And all the snow had
become so disturbed and excited
all over the earth, was now being drawn in one direction -
towards this white pillar that
grew higher and higher in the
shape of a funnel, a white
funnel of whirling snow that
was now so tall that however
far back I tilted my head I
couldn't see the top.   And
then, oh horror of hags! I saw
the snow was being pulled away
from beneath our very feet and
all about us, and worse than
that, we could feel our very
selves begin to be tugged towards the whirlwind. There
was nothing to hold on to.
Jackson was clinging on to my
leg, which made things even
more difficult; but I began to
dig deeper still in the snow
with great fury.   Every moment
it was more difficult, for it
seemed that there was a great
invisible hand dragging at us,
and suddenly my camera was
snatched away and sucked into
the whirling pillar.

I can remember very vividly
how it looked as it rushed
across the ground into the
middle of the white whirling
funnel and was carried up, up
into the heights, and how I
thought in a spasm of horror
of how I would feel being carried up after it to certain
death.   But I never stopped
digging, and all at once my
hands struck something hard,
something as smooth as ice.
It was ice.   And then it
was that my brain worked even
more quickly than the whirlwind!   I plucked the cork off
and jabbed my leg-spike as
hard as I could into the shining, rock-like
surface
of the
ice.

It hardly made a mark, but I
jabbed again in exactly the
same place, and then again.
On the fourth jab it seemed
to stick a little, and then
I told Jackson what to do.
Five times we were nearly
torn away from where we strug-
gled to keep our balance before Jackson understood.   He
took hold of my proper leg
by its foot and, crouching
down, began to stumble round
and round me, twisting me as
he went.   So there I was, with
my spike in the ice and Jackson screwing me in, for if you
have another look at the drawings I have made of my sword-
fish spike, you'll see how it
is in the form of a gigantic
screw.

Round and round went Jackson, and deeper and deeper went my legspike until I was knee-deep in ice.

At that very moment,
with a deep husky roar all
the snow that was left on the
ground for as far as eye could
see began to rush across the
ground, until every particle
of it was gathered into the
whirlwind, which billowed up
to even greater heights
with a cry like the death of
a mammoth.   And then, as
suddenly as it had started,
the commotion ceased.   We
were in a dead calm.   Nothing stirred.   Even the pillar
of snow seemed to be, for a moment like a pillar of motionless marble.

I had only a moment to
observe the effect, for the
silence was broken as the
pillow of snow began to fall
in a crushing weight of whiteness, dead as dead.   And as
it fell a great shape began
to form and raise itself rapidly while the snow descended,
until in an absolute silence
there stood against the sky
and half way up it, a cone of
dazzling snow where the pillar
had been with not a snowflake
out of place!

There we were. 'The world swept bare of snow. A landscape black and shining and the white, perfect and enormous hill away to our right. It made a fine picture, but Jackson looked as silly as ever, and I really could have whacked him for his lack of interest.

However, he was very much needed just then, for he had to unscrew me from the ice.

The chief nuisance was the
loss of my box-camera.   We
could see it, a tiny dot no
larger than a full-stop,

                right on top of
the new mountain; but of course
it was impossible to recover -
not only because it would be
so long a climb, but because
the soft snow would not take
so heavy a weight as mine
without dragging me into its
depths.   Thank heavens, I
still had my typewriter!

        My eiderdown had got a bit
torn and a certain amount of
my precious orchid-stalk tobac
co plucked out by the whirlwind, but I sewed the rent up
with my bone needle and some
cat-fish gut, which I use instead of cotton and we were
soon on our way again.

        I find that this letter is
taking longer than I thought,
so I'll continue tomorrow
when I've had a good sleep,

for I am proverbially tired.
Tomorrow's letter won't be a
new one exactly, but a contin-
uation of this.

   Goodnight, nephew.   I'm
half asle ep.

            Your Uncle.

Letter No 13.

It couldn't have been more
than eleven o'clock when J.
and I continued our way across
the black ice.   The whole
adventure of the whirlwind had
only taken about half an hour.
But now a sepia-coloured darkness began to **close around me,
and the feeling that**

I was entering dangerous country
grew strong again.

It was getting time for our
dinner, but somehow it is
pleasanter to eat among rocks,
or icebergs or even glaciers
which one can lean against than
sitting, exposed and alone, in
the middle of an ice-field.
with nothing else for miles.
One feels so conspicuous, especially when Jackson makes such
noises when he is feeding, and
covers his chin with gravy meal
after meal.

So we walked on until we
reached the base of a glacier
To our surpise, we found
a circle of frozen rocks and
in the middle was the owner
of the desolate place - the
hairiest and whitest polar bear
that I had ever seen.   I did
not know that they were ever
as huge as this one.   His
paws were enormous, with every
toe-nail like a carving-knife.

But his eyes seemed very small
and evil in his shaggy head,
like loganberries.

    We had no time to go back.
He had seen us.   With a growl
that made Jackson turn a most
beastly colour, he stood up
on his back legs.   Then he
roared and the rocks trembled
and blocks of ice crashed and
tinkled —— as they fell from
the glacier above, and hun-
dreds of echoes roared after
him and got fainter and fainter.

    Jackson was shaking like a
flag, and I was wondering what
I could do to save our lives.

I had left my harpoon behind the
door of the cave - which
was a very silly thing to
do - but it wouldn't have
been much use against so
huge a beast.   Nor could
my leg-spike jab him any
higher than his knee.   I
knew the way that bears killed people.   They take
them in their huge white hairy
arms as though they are going to kiss them and then
they hug them to death.

    I knew it was no good to
turn round and run, because
with my leg-spike I wouldn't
be fast enough to escape. So
I waited and hoped for in-
spiration.

The bear waddled up to me
and opened his mouth so that
I saw regions of wet crimson
which I do not like remembering.   I stared up at his
big white face and his evil
little loganberry eyes.   I
even took a step closer, although I hadn't decided what
to do.

Suddenly his huge arms
swept out on either side, em-
braced me and lifted me far
from the ground and hugged
me to his chest.   His hairs,
which were like those at the
end of a dressing-gown cord,
smothered my face.

I knew that within a moment
he would squeeze the breath
out of me,

— But my arms were
around him, too - or half
way around, at any rate, and
I suddenly began to tickle him
under his arms.   I expected
the squeeze to come at any
moment, but before he had time
to recover from his surprise,
I tickled him again, deeper
and fiercer than before and a
shudder ran all over him under his hide.

     Perhaps I imagined it, but
I think that his arms did
not hold me quite so tight as
he shuddered - but I could
not escape, of course.   I
summoned up all the strength
I had, for tickling a Polar
Bear becomes tiring; and strain-
ing every muscle of my fingers
I tickled him again.   I
have never tickled anything
before.   As I tickled the
shudder grew more and more
violent until it turned into a wriggle.   He wriggled
all over, his head high up in
the air and his eyes tightly
shut.   But I did not weaken.
My fingers worked until their

bones ached; and suddenly,
in a huge convulsion, I
heard a shrill, hairy scream
of laughter above my head.

   Then came the uncontrol-
lable wriggles again, an-
other gigantic scream as the
laughter came bursting out
of the bear's body until his
arms grew so weak that he let
me fall to the ground and
his legs grew so weak that he
flopped down beside me and,
rolling over on his back, he
roared and screamed so terri-
bly in his convulsions that I
thought it the right time for
us to escape.

So Jackson and I left him there in the middle of his great hollow home of ice, his paws beating

the ground weakly at his side and his enormous white body heaving, as his laughter grew and grew and was all mixed up with the echoes which it made.

And still we hadn't had dinner
and it was not until we had put at
least a dozen glaciers between
ourselves and the Polar
bear that we lit a fire
and prepared our meal.

It was past tea-time
when J. and I came to
that weird and crystal
region where everything I
had longed for happened -
everything I had searched the
world for - and yet how dif-
ferent it all was to what
I had expected.   And rather
sad, too; not that J. realized this.   Bash my blubber! how irritating he is
when there is tragedy in
the air.   He never notices
it.

But the air was thick with it - and with magic - and danger. I noticed J. sniffling the breeze, and he began to walk much closer to me than usual.

We were in a land of jaggedness. Ahead, and on every side, great glittering steeples of ice began to show above the horizon just as though we were approaching a city of glass churches.

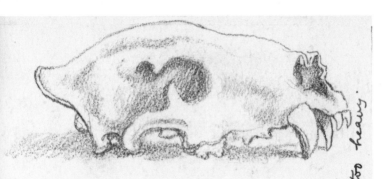

We left behind us the snow-
covered slopes, that were
littered with the skulls of
bears and the jawbones of
whales; and were on the
snowless, featureless
plains of ice again.   It
was dull and smooth-like
stone, but as we proceeded
it became clearer and
clearer and brighter and
brighter until we were as-
tonished.   All around us
was radiance.   As though
somebody had switched on
the electric light.   No,
not above us, as you would
expect.   Not the light of
the sky, which was inky-blue.
I mean below us - under the
ice we trod upon.   It had
become green - like an unripe
apple, and transparent - so
transparent that I blinked
and fidgeted with my eiderdown.   The underneath side
of Jackson's face was all
lit up with it.

For it seemed that we
were walking in the middle
of the air, for just beneath
us were three fish with teeth
like tombstones.   And there
was a shark with its ghastly
white stomach, and an octopus
that was gobbling up something that had purple blotches.
and eyes like soup-plates.
When J. saw these dreadful
things, just below our very
feet he climbed under my eider
down, where he shuddered and
made frightened noises.

Some puffins were watching us all the time which became rather embarrasing.

I had to carry him for quite a long time before I could get him to his feet again.   He was not easy to carry with all our belongings nailed to his back. He couldn't understand that the terrible sea creatures could not reach us through the clear green ice, although they looked as though they could.

At last I set him on his feet again and we continued our way over the ice that shone, now here, now there, now there with scarlet, yellow and silver lights as the monsters of the deep rose from the apple-green depths and burned like torches through a window-pane.

Of all the glass churches
with their glittering spikes,
there was only one which was
loftier and vaster by far
than all the others.   It
seemed silly to direct our
feet in any other direction.
When we were quite near we
found that there was an
island of snow on the ice
near the body of the great
glass church.   In the middle of the white island the
soft snow was heaved up into
a long hump not at all like
an ordinary hill, but a much
more exciting shape.   I did-
n't know then why I thought
it looked exciting, but I know
that I thought it would be
good to get to the top of it
and admire the view all round
before we explored the crystal
spires of the shining cathedral that shone above.

Within a few minutes we were
wading knee-deep in the snowy
island, with its white reflection in the green ice.   But
before we reached the white
hummocky shape in the rubble,
I began to feel very queer
indeed.   All sorts of memor-
ies rushed into my mind.   I
thought of tropical lands, of
rivers that steamed in the
African sun, and of the yellow
floods of water that try to
swallow China.   I thought
of all kinds of things suddenly as I stood there, and especi
ally of the White Lion whose
haunting presence in my mind
had changed my life and made
me one of the greatest explorers that the world has never
known.

And every time I thought
of the White Lion my heart began to knock like a bandit's
gong.   I had never felt
quite like this before and I
wondered why it should happen
now.

I looked this way and that
way but could see nothing to
make me feel so funny.   Perhaps an earthquake is going to
start, I thought, or a volcano
or even an avalanche.   But
the air was deadly silent.
Not a thing moved.   I listened
again with my head on one side
and then with my ear to the
snow (which is the best way),
but I couldn't hear anything.

Jackson was wrinkling his
nose and frowning and looking
very silly.   I pulled myself
together - gave Jackson a
sharp word of command and we
started to climb the hummocky
mound that seemed to shine ev-
en more whitely than anything
else in the whole landscape.

The snow got shallower at
once and was only just over
our ankles, and a few minutes
later not even our boots were
covered.   I had put the cork
on to the end of my leg-spike
when we arrived at the island

of snow, but it seemed to
slip more than usual, and
so did my ordinary foot, as
I climbed.   When we reached
the top we stared around us,
and still could see no reason
for the excitement which both
of us felt more than ever,
for even Jackson could not keep still for a minute but kept
sniffing at the white ground
we were standing on and muttering to himself. Somehow
the danger and magic which I
felt in my body was stronger
than ever up there on the
mound.

              We sat down and for the
         first time that day felt warm.
         We even took our gloves off,
         for the snow itself seemed to
         give out heat, which was very
         peculiar indeed.   I took off
         my bowler hat and scratched my
         head.   Then I put my hat on
         again.   Next I looked down at
         the soft snow island beneath
         us, some distance below, and I
         felt a great desire to get
         down there as quickly as I
         could although I could not
         think why.   Pickle my blubber
         and twang my gullet strings!
         but it was most odd.   Most
         odd indeed - and my spine was
         in a turmoil of shudders.

To calm myself I took out
my pipe, and finding the hole
in my eiderdown, pulled out
a handful of orchid-tobacco
and began to smoke.   And then!
- then! there was another shudder.   But it wasn't mine - and
it wasn't Jackson's.

The shudder was beneath us.
Beneath us!   It came out of
the warm hummocky white hill.
I shouted to Jackson: "It's an
earthquake!   Tie up your laces!"
For I knew how he was always
tripping up, even without earth-
quakes.   But directly I had
shouted this I knew I must be
wrong.   Because no earthquake
would take up such a little
space as just the hill we were
on but would spread for hun-
dreds of miles - and I knew that
the glass mountain, with all
the icy steeples, hadn't felt
it, for not an icicle tinkled.

i'm rather fond at blowing smoke-rings

It was as deadly silent as ever.
We had jumped to our feet, of
course, and now I was determined
to get down to the level snow
as fast as I could. Jackson
who seemed to have some kind
of instinct which he had never
used before, was half way down
the steep white slope already
with the typewriter, saucepans,
portmanteaux and so on, swinging and clanging on his back.

    I turned to follow him, but
my cork foot lost its grip and
before I knew where I was I
found myself tumbling head
over heels all the way down
the high soft flank of the
hill; but before I reached
the flat snow at the bottom,
the hill itself that I was
tumbling down shuddered
once more and began

to GET
UP !

When I had finished fall-
ing I was in the deep snow again and only my head was above
the surface.

It was turned the wrong way
and I found myself looking
at Jackson who seemed to be
smiling behind his hand. This
cou ld'nt have been so, because
he had never used any express-
ions before (except when the
Bear picked me up weeks ago
when I thought I saw the same
sort of smirk on his face but
that was his nervousness too,
I expect, or else colic.

I twisted my head
so that I could see over my
left shoulder, and there a-
gainst the sky with his mane
billowing out in a cloud of
white smoke and his eyes like
platters of gold fire was the
White Lion.

    I have tried to remember and
write down what I felt when I
saw him, but nothing has come
out right.   Anyway, you want
to know what happened next and
not what I felt, so perhaps
it is a good thing I can't ex-
press my terrible pride when
I saw him face to face for the
first time.   Not that he saw
my face - I was too far below
him, and he was nearly blind.
I could see this at once.   His
huge gold eyes were quite empty looking, for he was past
his prime and was ready to die.

But the shaggy and dazzling
whiteness of his Arctic fur
was something I shall never
forget. Even the snow
looks dirty and grey to me
when I remember the White
Lion.

    I had forgotten about Jack-
son, and was very annoyed
when, after looking everywhere
for him, I found that he had
hidden himself under my eiderdown

    It only shows how much my
thoughts were concentrated on
the White Lion when you realize that I had never even felt
him *although he must have wriggled.*When
I had plucked him out, his
teeth were still chattering,
and I could not convince him
for a long time that the White
Lion was nearly blind.

Just then the sun began to
sink and there were coloured
crosses and circles in the
sky - the Hairy-Bleary-Alice
or something like that they
call it, and I was very struck
with it when I first saw it,
with all the sky lit up
like fireworks.   Anyway,
as soon as the sun sank
the White Lion shook his
mane and half the sky was
hidden with it as it swung
to and fro.   And then he
bridled up his noble head
and began to pace to the
cathedral of glass with its
twenty thousand spires.   In
spite of his blindness he
never made a faulty step but
trod on and on in the deep
snow until the ice began and
then on and on over the ice,
while I followed him on tiptoe
with Jackson at my heels.

The White Lion turned to
the East when he reached the
f̶e̶e̶t̶ foot of the Cathedral,
and padded towards a high
narrow opening with icicles
hanging from its roof. When
he reached this entrance he
stopped and lowered his head
to the ice. Then he coughed
out a little rumbling roar,
the smallest he could make,
and this little roar ran like
a boulder over the glass and
into the interior, where I
heard it leap and toss itself
about with a hundred thousand
echoes. It was a kind of
warning - like someone makes
when they want some more cake
at tea-time.

But who could the white
Lion be wanting to warn?   I
could not think.   But there
he was, his mouth near the
green and shining ice and his
forehead wrinkled like a pillow in the early morning as
though he was listening. Then
he moved like a white and
soundless cloud ~~into~~ through
the opening in the glassy walls.
~~Then~~ we followed on tip-toe.
For a long time it was very
dark and colder than I could
believe, and then gradually
the walls grew further apart
and the darkness became green,
and the green became lighter
and brighter, until suddenly
we were in a vast hall, but
huger than a hall, more like
a theatre, or the inside of a
cathedral as I have called it
before.

As it was when Jackson and
I first saw the fishes under
the sea, so it was now.   The
light shone from below, for the
ice at our feet was transparent
again, and all along the
length of the cathedral floor,
and clear as though there was
no ice at all, lay a whale as
long as a street.   It was
quite motionless except for
its fins, which twitched every
now and then to scare away the
little crimson fishes that
darted here and there.   On the
ice, a few yards above the
whale's head, and far away
on the cathedral floor was
a rough and dusky throne of
ice, and as the White Lion
paced his way to it he held
his head very high, although
he was so tired after so
long and fabulous a life.

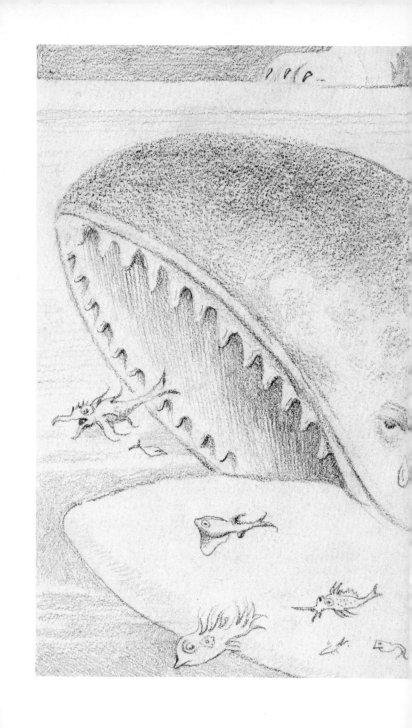

On every side were glassy
terraces. The mountain
which I had thought was made
of solid ice was quite hollow, and far above me the
green dusk reached right up
to the welkin, and filled
the empty pinnacles with its
colour.

But the great whale that
brooded beneath the floor was
not the only living creature
who was watching the Lion as
he neared the icy throne.
Oh no. I saw a vast and
silent congregation.

For sitting on the terra-
ces of crystal that rose on
every side were Arctic Beasts
and Polar Fowl, Bears, Wolves
and Elks; Seals; Reindeer and white
crows; snow-serpents and
every kind of polar creature.

and the water beneath the ice
was thickening with fish until it was no longer green,
but trembled with all the
colours of the rainbow.

But although everything
else reflected the colours
that smould$ered through the
ice - the Lion didn't. Nothing could change his whiteness. He was apart from
everything else.

When he reached the top
of the throne his eyes burned and he shook his mane for
the last time, and as it
tossed in a tempest of white
string, it hissed in the
cathedral silence like a
hundred snakes.

And then it happened. He
reared up on his hind legs,
opened his great jaws, spread
his paws as big as white has-
socks against the air and
with a roar that set the
high spires jangling - froze
to death.

He had become ice. He
had crystallized. It does
not matter what words I use
to describe it, for there he
was, and there he will be for
ever, alone and beautiful
in the wild polar waste -
alone in his cathedral, my
Lion of white ice.

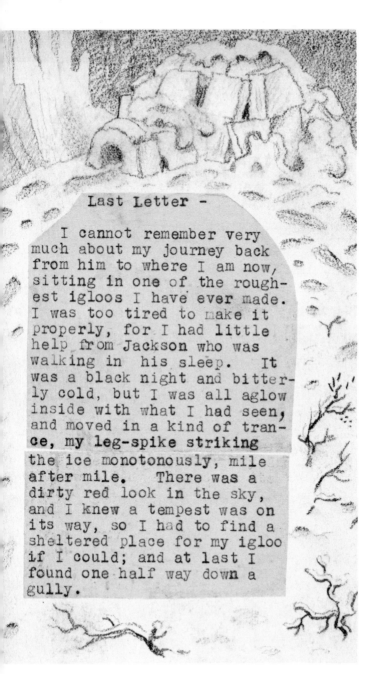

Last Letter -

I cannot remember very
much about my journey back
from him to where I am now,
sitting in one of the rough-
est igloos I have ever made.
I was too tired to make it
properly, for I had little
help from Jackson who was
walking in his sleep.   It
was a black night and bitter-
ly cold, but I was all aglow
inside with what I had seen,
and moved in a kind of tran-
ce, my leg-spike striking
the ice monotonously, mile
after mile.   There was a
dirty red look in the sky,
and I knew a tempest was on
its way, so I had to find a
sheltered place for my igloo
if I could; and at last I
found one half way down a
gully.

The one thing I am anxious about now is that you really get this letter and give the facts to the Natural History Museum. If only my camera had not been swept up in the whirlwind I might possibly have got a snap of him on his throne, but I don't know. Somehow I didn't want to do anything except look and look and look.

The Esquimaux stamp which is on the envelope gives you a slight idea of him, and of his whiteness, but not of his size and importance.

Well, Nephew, I must end
this letter.   I didn't think
I wanted to write it at first
but I am glad I have persev-
ered.   Pickle my blubber!
but I feel quite a literary
light.

Maybe one day I'll turn
up in England.   In the mean-
while there is everything in
the world that I enjoy, all
around me the sledges the kyaks
the seals and killer whales.
Jackson has just come in
through the igloo doorway.
He looks a bit excited.   Oh,
Blubber, how clumsy he is -
tripping over my tee-spike
again and spilling all the
coffee over this page.   Oh,
Blubber him!

I have been out to see w
what he is so excited
about.   It was only a herd
of reindeer

fighting with wolves. As
though I hadn't seen that
sort of thing often enough
without being disturbed.
However, I think I could do
with another wolf-skin, as
the one I have lined my bowler hat with is almost in
shreds.

So I must sharpen my sword-spike and then be off, neph-ew.

So goodbye.

from your **Lost Uncle**

First published in 1948
by Eyre and Spottiswoode (Publishers) Ltd
Text and illustrations copyright 1948
under the Berne Convention by Mervyn Peake
This edition published in 1976
by Methuen Children's Books Ltd
11 New Fetter Lane, London EC4P 4EE
© 1976 by Maeve Peake
All rights reserved
Printed in Great Britain by
Fletcher & Son Ltd, Norwich

ISBN 0 416 56540 9